HOMIES,
Lovers,
FRIENDS...
& MURDER

HOMIES, Lovers, FRIENDS... & MURDER

PATRICK L. TURNER

"Everybody ain't yo friend,
Everybody ain't yo patna..."

3

CONTENTS

RIME SCENE - DO NOT CROSS

HOMIES, *Lovers,* & FRIENDS

It all started in the early 90's, in Santa Monica, California, at King Max's house. King Max was the number one DJ in the hood. He threw house parties in his backyard, and this was one of the most infamous house parties in the history of Santa Monica. There were three fights, a house got shot up, there was a beat down, and a cutting.

The first fight was over a girl named Tasha. This was when the movie Harlem Nights was out. In the movie, there was a woman named 'Lady Heroin,' aka *Sunshine*. They said that her lovin' was so good that when you throw it in the air, it turned into *sunshine*. After the fight between these two guys, they started calling Tasha '*Sunshine!*'

The second fight, well we could call it more of a beat down, started because there was a white boy at the party, and he was a Crip. He said the derogatory term for Bloods, which is "slob," and the whole party and neighborhood were Bloods! So, once he said that he realized where he was, but it was too late.

He took off running out of the door with the whole party chasing him down the street. They caught him and beat him down in the middle of the street. He got up, staggered into somebody's house, then somebody shot the house up. No one was killed; everyone went back to the party, and it continued.

The next fight is what started everything. I

don't know the details of why it started. All I know is I turned around and I saw my homie, AC, fighting with another homie, from the Street Legend Posse. It was Hakeem's brother.

Hakeem's brother hit AC in the head with a bumpy face Gin bottle. It slid down, broke, and cut an artery in AC's forearm! AC hopped in his all-red, brand new, custom Blazer with IROC rims, with a custom-made sliding rag top with the booming system. Me and Dontae hopped in the blazer with AC.

AC drove himself to the hospital because me and Dontae couldn't drive. Blood was squirting out of his arm like a faucet. By the time we got to the hospital, he had almost fainted.

We ran inside to get the paramedics. They ran out and got AC. They took him in for emergency surgery. Inside of the Blazer the entire floor, front and back, was covered in blood!

While me and Dontae were waiting in the hospital room along with everybody else who showed up, a detective came in asking questions about the shooting. Of course, nobody knew anything. The detective asked questions about AC's fight. Nobody knew anything. So, they left.

Because of what happened there was now beef between Hakeem's brother, the Street Legend Posse, and AC. Everybody would end up having to choose sides.

The next week, we met at the club, and it was supposed to be Hakeem's brother's side against AC's side. AC's side showed up deep and ready to rumble. Hakeem's brother never showed up. Later on, they talked and squashed the beef. This is when AC decided to start his own crew.

A couple of weeks passed, and we were at AC's apartment talking. AC said he had it all figured out. He said that he was going to take his crew to another level and that he was going to promote his own party productions.

We sat there trying to help him think of a name for the new crew. At that time, AC's favorite artist was R Kelly. R Kelly's song "Homie Lover Friend" was playing.

I said, "That's it! That's what we're going to name the crew – Homies, Lovers, & Friends."

Everybody who would attend the events was going to be homies, some would bring their mates, so there would be lovers, and of course, friends. AC liked the idea. He agreed and **HOMIES,** *Lovers*, & FRIENDS a.k.a. **H L F** was born!

~As told by Jay Love
An original member of H L F

RIME SCENE - DO NOT CROSS

PREFACE

The Legacy Tribune

BODY OF MAN FOUND

❡SANTA MONICA, CA - Homicide investigators are looking into the death of an unidentified black man whose body was found...at approximately 12:15 pm by hospital security officers. "We are treating it at this point as a homicide...the victim had trauma to the body. The cause of death is to be determined by an autopsy."

The body was that of a 6-foot-tall, approximately 220-pound man in his late 20s to early 30s.

Finally, after being on hold for about 10 minutes, they came back on the phone. They said they took a lot of fingerprints from his truck and the set of fingerprints that belonged to him matched the body they found on Sunday.

"We are sorry. Please tell your brother that unfortunately the body found is that of Devin Cole. Also, let him know that Devin's family hasn't been notified yet because they haven't been home. You two are the first to know that Devin has passed."

My sister looked at me, nodded her head, and in a low, soft tone said, "Yes, Anthony. It's Devin."

I went into shock. My sister hugged me, and we both cried.

***

RIME SCENE - DO NOT CROSS

CHAPTER 1

NOVEMBER 1, 1997 - I was at this popular nightclub in Santa Monica. My friend, Hakeem, approached me and told me that he had just bailed my homeboy RB out of jail.

"Who?" I asked.

"Your homeboy, RB. Tank just told me that RB was broke."

"What do you mean he's broke?"

"Yeah, that's what I'm hearing. He's broke, but I didn't hear that until after Lola had already bailed him out."

I think I was more shocked hearing about RB not having money than hearing about him being in jail.

I had known RB for 12 years. For five years, he had this hookup working for a warehouse. That particular warehouse is no longer in business, but back then, it would be compared to Best Buy, on a smaller scale.

RB worked in the shipping and receiving department from 1992 to 1997. From what I remember, they would overstock the appliances and sell the merchandise on the street for the low. They would make a nice profit, and they did this for at least five years.

Hakeem couldn't tell me what RB went to jail for, but I knew he was more upset hearing that RB was broke. He probably wouldn't have his money back from bailing him out by Tuesday like he promised Lola.

Hakeem said if RB didn't have the money

by Tuesday, there was going to be some problems. He said he only gave Lola the money to bail RB out because he thought he still had money.

RB was a friend of mine. I had known him since high school. We graduated together in 1986 and remained good friends up until about 1997. Hakeem was a friend of a friend who we all used to hang around, go to parties with, play sports with, and have social gatherings with. Hakeem and I also worked together. We were cool, but RB and Hakeem were only friends through me, so there was no connection between the two guys other than myself.

On November 3, 1997, two days after seeing Hakeem at the club, I was at work, standing on the dock, waiting for my work assignment. I saw Hakeem walking through the parking lot and through the gate. As he got closer, I could see he looked frustrated.

"What's good, bro?" I asked.

He replied, "I've been hearing RB is broke for the past two days. He is supposed to have my money by tomorrow, but from what I'm hearing, he's broke."

I was still trying to fathom how RB went broke after all the money I knew he made over the years selling those appliances.

Later that evening, I called Devin so I could tell him what Hakeem had been telling me. Over the past few years, RB and Devin had gotten pretty close. Devin had become RB's right-hand man after Devin lost his job working for a truck rental company.

At one time, I was the guy who RB would ask to help get rid of his appliances, but because of my popularity – and after RB started noticing that I was making just as much money as him on his stuff – he eventually cut me out. He started going straight to my plug, a guy named Dino.

Dino was an older Hispanic who lived across the street from Devin, Shawn, and me when we were all roommates in Venice. Dino would buy everything I had, and he would sell it just as fast as RB would give it to me. Dino would often ask when I would have more, so it was like clockwork. It was a guaranteed sale when it came to Dino.

RB would ask me how I was selling appliances so fast. When I told him about Dino, he started meeting with him. That's pretty much how RB cut me out and stopped fronting appliances to me.

RB started using Devin because he was out of work at the time and had a truck. So, when I went to meet with Devin about RB, he told me that RB was indeed broke.

"How? How did he go broke?" I asked Devin.

Devin explained that RB was tricking his money off for years. He had been buying clothes, renting high-end cars every weekend, and sponsoring trips to Las Vegas, Nevada. He also rented limos and had a car custom built.

Devin told me that one night they counted $283,000 together, so he knew RB had a lot of money, but he had blown it all. I was shocked to hear how much RB had at one point. I had no idea it was that much, and to hear that it was all gone was crazy!

"I talked to RB earlier today, and he said he was going to give Hakeem his money on Tuesday," Devin said.

"I hope so because I am tired of hearing Hakeem's mouth talking about if's and but's," I replied.

***

Tuesday morning came, and it looked like the same scene as the day before. Hakeem came walking through the gate with that same look.

He said, "AC, today is the day RB is supposed to have my money. But for some reason, I don't think he's going to have it."

I said, "I talked to Devin last night, and he was pretty much saying the same thing, that RB is broke."

"I don't care if he's broke. He better have my $1,500 by this evening," Hakeem told me.

CRIME SCENE - DO NOT CROSS

CHAPTER 2

Before we went out of work that day, Hakeem and I were in the backyard of the facility, just killing time, when we decided to call RB.

Hakeem said, "Hey man, I'm about to call this nigga to see if he has the money because after work I'm going straight to his house."

Hakeem grabbed his phone and called RB.

"I'm going to put the speaker on so you can hear him."

The phone rang a couple of times before RB answered.

"Hello?"

"What's up, RB?" Hakeem started.

"Shit. Nothing, just chilling. What's good, Hakeem?"

"Bro, it's almost 3 p.m., and I'm about to get off work to come get my money. Do you have my money? Because for the past two days, all I've been hearing is how broke you are."

RB replied, "Man, I told you that I was going to have your money by today, so why are you trippin?"

Hakeem said, "Nigga, I'm trippin? I just want my money, but I'm hearin you broke."

"I'm going to pay you your money today, and when I do, after today, don't call my ass anymore."

"Nigga, call you? For what? You're not my homeboy, you're AC's homeboy! Me and you never kicked it like that, and you never fucked with me like that, nigga! Back in the day when you were selling those TV's and shit, you never sold me shit, so nigga, I won't ever call your ass again. I just want my money. I'll see you around 4 p.m., and if you don't have my money, you'll see."

RB didn't respond and just hung up.

***

The next day was a Wednesday. For the third day in a row, here comes Hakeem, walking through the gate again, but this time I could actually see red in his eyes. He looked like he had a rough night.

I was hoping that the crazy shit with RB was finally over, but boy, was I in for a surprise.

As Hakeem got closer, he started shaking his head. He looked pissed.

"What's good, Hakeem?" I asked. "Bro, please don't tell me RB didn't pay you your money."

Hakeem screamed, "Fuck no! Man, this nigga tried to have me set up!"

"What?!"

"Yeah, man, let's go to the backyard. I don't want anyone in my business."

We had coworkers standing around the dock as we were waiting for our work assignments. We walked to the backyard, where there were tables that we could hang out at when we had nothing to do or when it was raining.

Hakeem said, "Man, this nigga tried to

have me set the fuck up."

"How? What happened?"

"When I went by his house, he came out of his apartment and told me that he had my money. But we had to meet someone at the trolley station in Santa Monica on 3rd Street. So, I asked, 'What?' and RB said this guy owed him $2,000, and he was going to meet us there. I told him he better not be fucking around."

Then, Hakeem said, "I told him I didn't have time for no bullshit, and he said everything was good. So, we got in the car, and RB had a bad odor. He smelled like he had been drinking, and I wasn't cool with that. When we got there, RB asked if he could use my phone to call the guy. We waited 15 to 20 minutes, and no one showed up. RB went to call him again, but then after another 10 to 15 minutes, still no one showed up."

Hakeem told me he thought it was a set up, so he reached under his seat and pulled out his handgun to put it on his lap. RB saw the handgun and panicked. He asked Hakeem why he pulled out his gun, and he told RB he didn't trust him.

Hakeem ended up calling the guy they were waiting on, got his address, and they drove to his house. Hakeem said RB looked nervous but didn't say anything.

Once they arrived at the guy's house, RB got out of the car, headed up to the house and rang the doorbell. Hakeem said a brotha who was about 6'2" answered the door and came out. After a few minutes, he noticed the guy & RB shook hands. He said it looked like the guy handed RB some money, but Hakeem said he couldn't tell how much. After RB got the money, he walked back over to Hakeem's car and got in and told Hakeem he got it, and they could go.

Hakeem said, "So, I told RB thanks and started counting the money he handed me. I noticed that he only handed me $900! I told him, 'Nigga this is only $900! You owe me $600 more, and if that nigga owes you $2,000, you better ask him for at least another $600 so you can pay me.' Well, RB told me he would have the rest in a few days, but I told him, 'Fuck no! I want all my money right now!' I told him I was going out of town on Thursday, and I needed all of it."

Hakeem said that RB told him he would have his money, but Hakeem didn't accept that. He turned his car around and headed back to the guy's house. He told me that RB was trying to talk him out of it, but he wasn't listening to him. When they got there, Hakeem was the one to get out of the car this time and go up to the house.

"So, the guy answered, and I explained how RB owed me money and told me that he owed RB $2,000, so I brought him over to get paid. I asked the guy if he could give RB at least another $600 so RB could pay me. Well turns out, RB lied to me, and this guy only owed him $900 for three pounds of marijuana."

As Hakeem was talking to this guy, the guy snatched the $900 from his hands.

Hakeem responded, "Nigga, I don't even know you like that, and I don't fuck with niggas I don't know."

Hakeem and the guy both were hot! They walked over to Hakeem's car and confronted RB. He was sitting in the car looking straight ahead, looking scared. He didn't have shit to say.

Hakeem said he got in his car, took out his gun again, and told RB that he didn't appreciate trying to have him set up, and that could have ended badly. He told him he better come up with his money ASAP! RB told Hakeem that his sister was coming to town and that he would get the money from her so everything would be squashed.

"I told him this would be his last chance to have my money because I am going out of town on Thursday. RB promised me he will have it."

I was tripping after what I just heard from Hakeem. I couldn't believe RB put Hakeem through all that shit.

That night, I called Devin and told him everything Hakeem told me.

Devin said, "That is crazy. RB reached out to me last night, and I am going to take a signed check from his sister tomorrow and deposit the check to get the money to pay off Hakeem."

"That's cool because there's no telling what Hakeem is going to do at this point," I said.

CRIME SCENE - DO NOT CROSS

CHAPTER 3

The next day, I talked to Devin again. He told me that he had met up with RB's sister, and she wrote him a check for $1,500. He went to his bank and cashed it. Later that afternoon, he met up with Hakeem and paid him off. When I heard that, I was just glad that it was all over.

***

The weekend came and went. Everything was good until Tuesday, November 9th, when I received a call from Devin.

"Hey, AC, what's up?"

"What's good, Devin?"

"Man, you're not going to believe this."

"Oh boy, what now?"

Devin replied, "Why did I just go to my bank to withdraw some money out, and I have negative $800?"

"What? What happened?"

"That $1,500 check RB's sister wrote me bounced, and now I have a negative $800 balance."

Devin was pissed, and that was not like him. You rarely saw him upset.

"I'm done trying to look out for RB. I am going to call him and tell him if they don't have all my money back by Friday, I am going to take them to court and sue them for twice as much money as they got from me."

Devin continued, "I just got my life back on track after moving back with my parents. I just finished going to trade school to learn how to install fiber optics and just got a job offer. My days dealing with RB are over, but I will still help him when I can."

At this point, I was really starting to think something was going on with RB because of what he did to Hakeem and now Devin.

***

Three days passed. Devin called me late Friday night. He told me he was out with Jessica Boyd, and they were downtown in Los Angeles hanging out and enjoying some of the Classic Weekend festivities. This was an annual event that was in Pasadena, California annually. They hosted parties, parades, and it ended with a football game. We enjoyed attending this weekend event any time we could.

Friday night kicked off that weekend. Saturday morning was the parade. After the parade, the game would be played at the Rose Bowl. Devin told me that he wanted to tailgate at the Classic game on Saturday. He said that he was going to barbecue some pollo asado, and that he would call me the next morning.

That Saturday morning, I received a call from Devin at about 7 a.m. He told me that he had gotten off the phone with RB, and that he had his money.

"I am about to head over to his house and get that $1,500 he owes me. After that, I am going to stop at a store to pick up the pollo asado for the tailgate party. Let's meet at Shawn's house around noon."

"OK, I don't know where he lives, but I will call him and get the address."

We got off the phone, not knowing that would be the last time we spoke.

CRIME SCENE - DO NOT CROSS

CHAPTER 4

The football game was at 3:30 p.m. that day, so we had about two to three hours to tailgate. After I got off the phone with Devin, I received a call from Jamarcus Wilson, who owned a cell phone business with me. Jamarcus asked me if I wanted to ride with him to take a look at a car. I agreed and got dressed so I could meet him.

When I arrived, Jamarcus was waiting for me.

I said, "I want to have my Ford Expedition washed while we are gone."

So, Jamarcus and I took a drive and returned to the car wash around 10:15 a.m. I paid for the car wash, and Jamarcus and I parted ways.

I headed up toward John Muir High School to catch the tail end of the parade before going to Shawn's house. John Muir High School was predominately black. The school was a central part of the Classic festivities.

On my way to the parade, I received a call from Shawn.

He said, "Devin just called and said he was at RB's house but mentioned you guys are planning to meet over at my house before we head to the game."

"Yeah, that was the plan."

"Do you have my address?"

"No but let me call you back after I get to the parade."

When I got to the parade, it was pretty

much over. I pulled up to the gas station, and some guy was selling tickets to the football game. I bought four tickets for Shawn, Shawn's son Little Shawn, Devin, and myself for $15 each.

While I was at the gas station, I ran into my homeboy Rico Tenison. Rico used to date my older sister, Sherise, and he and I worked together.

We chatted for a few minutes, then he asked, "What do you have going on for the rest of the day?"

"Shawn, Devin, and I are going to the Classic game. I am about to head over to Shawn's house to meet them."

"You know Shawn moved, right?" Rico mentioned.

"Yeah," I replied.

"Do you know where he lives?"

I told him I didn't know, and he said he would take me over there. When we made it to Shawn's house, he came outside.

"Hey, that nigga RB has been calling me, talking about how he wanted to go to the football game with us."

"How does he even know we are going to the game?"

"I don't know, maybe Devin told him because he was over there when he called me earlier," Shawn explained.

"I'm not fucking with that nigga because he

left me hanging and was supposed to help me move into my house, so fuck him!"

"Yeah, I remember that. That was fucked up, and that's supposed to be your boy. I am not fucking with RB either because he was hollering at one of my bitches behind my back on some playa-hatin type shit. But I'm not trippin, it was just how he was telling her that I had other bitches and that she wasn't the only one. That wasn't cool. So, she called me telling me how he was talking to her sister, too, and I guess that's why she was telling me. She told me that she would call him on the three-way so that I could hear what he had to say about me."

Back in the day, the fellas would call that dirty mackin,' and that's against the guy code. We don't do that shit, but if you got game, and she choose, then she's free game, but that wasn't the case.

Later that evening, Carmen, the female I was talking to called me and told me that she was going to call RB on the three-way.

"Go ahead. I want to hear what he has to say," I told her.

She called RB, and he answered.

"What's up?"

She started talking about how she was upset with him because she knew that he was taking her sister out and using her sister. She also talked about how he was talking shit about me.

He never denied any of it and only said, "Your sister and I are just friends."

He also mentioned to her that I was still seeing my son's mother and had other women on the side. I couldn't believe what I was hearing because I had known RB for 12 years, and we had never had any problems. I felt betrayed, and I was disappointed in RB.

I never spoke up on the three-way call because she told me not to say anything, but I decided I would address him later, and I did. I called RB and told him that I was on the phone when Carmen called, and he still denied everything.

"That was fucked up. If you have action with her, then get at her, but you shouldn't have mentioned me," I told him.

That was probably the last time I heard from RB until Hakeem told me he bailed him out, and if I had to guess, I would say that was around July or August of 1997.

RIME SCENE - DO NOT CROSS

CHAPTER 5

While we were still at Shawn's house waiting for Devin, Shawn went in the house periodically to do whatever he was doing to get ready for the tailgate and game. He would come back out and tell me RB was calling again, wanting to go to the game. We both agreed again that we weren't fucking with RB.

It was about 12 p.m., and we still hadn't heard from Devin. I called him a few times, and it was getting closer to game time with no answer. I decided to leave him a message.

"Hey Devin, we're over at Shawn's house waiting for you, homie. Give me a call and let me know if we're still meeting up."

Devin never returned my call, so at that point, I thought he was somewhere taking care of business and would meet us at the game.

Once again, Shawn came back outside and said, "Blood, this nigga keeps calling me about this game."

I was like, "Man, fuck it, just let his ass come. It'll be like a little homies' reunion, and maybe we all can get some shit off our chests."

"OK, y'all can just kick it here at my house while I go to the train station and get him."

Shortly after, Shawn went to get RB. I tried calling Devin a few more times. When Shawn brought RB to the house, I was going to ask him where Devin went after he left his house. This wasn't like Devin.

Shawn made it back with RB. They pulled

up into Shawn's driveway, parked, and got out. It was a weird feeling seeing RB in the flesh after hearing so much about him over the past two weeks. I hadn't personally seen him in a few months.

"What's up, AC?" RB said.

"What's up, RB? What's good with you?"

I looked at him to see if he looked like he was broke or going through something. To me, he looked the same – he may have gained a few pounds. He was about 250 pounds, 5'9", with a big stomach, brown skin, and short fade.

He said, "Man, I've just been chillin."

"That's what's up," I replied. "Hey, where did Devin go after he left your house? We've been waiting for him, and he was supposed to meet us over here about two hours ago. Wasn't he at your house earlier?"

He looked shocked.

"Yeah, he came through, but he left. When I left my house to go to the store, I saw him talking to some dude driving a blue Honda Accord dressed in an orange jumpsuit. Don't the city Sanitation Department guys wear orange?"

"Yes, they do," I said.

"Devin did mention that he was going to meet up with these girls at a local radio station – to pick up some tickets to the football game tomorrow."

"That's funny because he told me the other day that he couldn't get any tickets to the game."

"Man, I don't know. You know how Devin be lying."

"It's good, but we need to start heading to this game. I guess we'll just have to meet Devin there."

"Well, I need a ticket."

"I bought Devin a ticket, but since he's not here, you could buy it."

"How much do you want for it?"

"$15 because that's what I bought it for."

He agreed and reached into his pocket, pulling out a nice wad of money. The first thing that came to mind was that he paid Devin, and the mess was finally over.

CRIME SCENE - DO NOT CROSS

CHAPTER 6

RB told me he wanted to stop by the indoor swap meet to pick up a fresh, white T-shirt and something to drink. I agreed. Shawn and Little Shawn came out of the house and got into the back of my Ford Expedition. RB got into the passenger seat, and we headed to the swap meet.

Once we arrived, RB got out while Shawn, Little Shawn, and I stayed in the SUV. RB was in the swap meet for about 10 minutes. When he got back in the car, he wanted to stop by the liquor to get something to drink. Once again, we stayed in the vehicle and waited. Once RB got back in the car again, we were on our way to the stadium.

We arrived at the Rose Bowl around 2:45 p.m., and it looked like everyone was packing up their tailgate parties and heading inside. The game started around 3:30 p.m. I was sure people wanted to see all the festivities on the field before the game started.

Right before we parked, my son's mother called me and asked, "Are you still tailgating? We just arrived with Sherise, Tony, and David."

"No, we're not tailgating because we were waiting for Devin to show up over at Shawn's house, but he never made it," I told her.

We both parked, but we went our separate ways once we got inside.

The game was packed as expected, and as we were walking around, heading toward our seats, we noticed the Street Legend Posse up ahead. The Street Legend Posse was the same group of friends that Hakeem was part of. Hakeem wasn't there that day because I assumed he was out of town like he said he would be, taking care of business.

As we approached the Street Legend Posse, I remember RB walking slowly and staying back.

He said something like, "Hey, I'm just going to walk down toward the plaza level to avoid those guys because I'm not in the mood. I don't want them to start basing on me."

Basing is a term we used; it means playing the dozen, and we did that almost every time we were together.

We had a brief encounter with the Street Legend Posse, then we headed to our seats. By the time we made it there, RB was already sitting in his seat.

***

After the game, we headed back to my car. I drove to drop off Shawn, Little Shawn, and RB. It was Saturday night and I had planned on going to the club that night. I asked RB and Shawn if they wanted to go, but Shawn couldn't go because his wife, Amerie, probably wasn't going to let him. RB said that he would go, but he had something to take care of that night. I told them that we could all get together another time and hang out like old times. They both agreed.

RB explained that he had stopped coming around because he didn't really care too much about the younger guys who started coming around. He said he didn't know them like that. The younger guys he was talking about were all about five years younger than I was and I was around 29, but they were good guys and just wanted to be around and have fun like everyone else.

We arrived at Shawn's house, and they all got out. At that point, it was about 9 p.m. Once I made it home, I got dressed, and headed to the nightclub. I stayed at the club until closing time.

RIME SCENE - DO NOT CROSS

CHAPTER 7

I made it home early Sunday morning around 3 a.m. and I went to sleep. A few hours later, I was awakened by a phone call. It was from RB.

He said that he was over at his Aunt's house. He mentioned that he was walking over by Devin's house. I cut him off and told him that I had just made it in from the club, I was sleeping, and to call me back.

"OK, I'll call you back in a couple of hours," he said.

I went back to sleep but was awakened by another phone call not even two hours later. It was RB, again.

"Are you up, yet?" he asked.

"No," I replied.

"Well, I saw Johnny this morning. And I saw Devin's truck blocking the driveway at his house."

"I was sleeping! Call me back," I said.

We hung up and I fell back asleep, only to be awakened, again, by a call from RB. It was now around 10:30 a.m.

"You up, yet?"

I was a little irritated, but I was curious to see what he wanted to talk about because he was so persistent.

"What's up?" I mumbled.

RB asked, "What do you have up for today? Are you going somewhere to watch the game?"

"No, I had planned on watching the game

at my sister Dana's house."

I was staying with her at the time.

"Is that all you wanted? You have been blowing up my phone all morning."

"I am over at my Aunt Sheila's house, and she lives near Devin. I was out walking. When I walked down his street, I noticed his black Nissan hard body pickup was parked in front, but the truck was blocking the driveway."

"So, what's wrong with that?"

"I just thought it was weird, so I went and knocked on the door to see why his truck was parked like that. No one answered, so I just walked away. But when I got to the end of the sidewalk, Devin's dad came to the door and asked how he could help me. I asked for Devin, and he said he wasn't home. I told his dad that Devin's truck was blocking the driveway and I thought it was odd. He asked if I could move it because he couldn't drive a manual."

"OK," I responded.

He mentioned that he also saw Johnny that morning, but he didn't say much else about that.

RB then told me to call the homies and see if they wanted to get together for the game.

"I'm sure everyone already has plans. It's already close to noon," I told him.

"Just call up a couple homies and see."

I called Dontae first. He said he already had plans. Then, I called Tank and Shawn, who were also busy. RB asked me to hook up with him. He wanted to go to this particular restaurant to watch the game. I really didn't want to go because I wanted to stay at home, but he was persistent. RB and I are both huge Raiders' fans, so I figured we could go and watch our boys play.

The game didn't start until 6 p.m., so we had some time before heading to the restaurant. I told RB I would pick him up around 4 p.m. because I had to go and buy my dogs some food. I told him I would call him when I was on my way to him.

"Just call me when you get close, and I will be waiting on the corner. The security guard be trippin'," RB said.

I agreed. Then, I recalled talking to Hakeem, who mentioned that one time before he bailed RB out of jail, he went by RB's house to pick up a 70-inch TV. He said when he got there, RB was already outside with it. He wasn't sure why he had the TV outside and why he couldn't just go inside and get it. Later, Devin and Tank said RB's apartment was jacked up and smelled bad. They said that RB was living foul, so because of that, I knew he didn't want me to come to his apartment, but I was cool with it.

I called RB when I was about two minutes away and he said that he'd be outside waiting for me. When I arrived, RB was there on the corner, waiting for me just like he said. He got in the truck, and we were off.

The first stop we had to make was Takari's house. I had to stop by there to drop off the dog food for my dog. She had been watching her because I had just moved out of my house a few blocks away just a month earlier. I had three Rottweilers; Takari had my puppy, Moet, and I had Rage and Bull with me at my sister's house.

After we dropped off the dog food at Takari's house, we stopped by my sister Sherise's house. We sat and talked to Sherise for about 30 minutes before we headed to the restaurant to watch the game.

CRIME SCENE - DO NOT CROSS

CHAPTER 8

When we got to the restaurant it was packed. This was a rival game between the Raiders and Chargers. RB and I sat at a table for two and we started ordering food and drinks as the game started.

The Raiders were doing their thing and winning the game. RB and I were high fiving each other every time the Raiders scored or whenever they made a big play. I think I had about two drinks, but I noticed RB was drinking heavily that night. In the years I had known RB, I had never seen him drink like that, but of course, I hadn't been around him in months and I knew he was probably going through something especially since people kept saying he was broke. I didn't stop to ask him about his drinking or anything because we were both into the game.

The game ended and the Raiders won. Our tab came up to around $90 and I only had about $35 on me. I asked RB could he cover me until I went to the bank, and he said he could. RB pulled out a wad of money just like he did the day before and I thought to myself, "*RB is back on top doing his thing.*"

We left the restaurant, and I headed straight to my bank so that I could pay RB back his money. After that, I drove to drop him off. When we got to his apartment, he told me to let him out at the corner because I'd probably get lost coming out. I just laughed as he got out of

HOMIES, *Lovers*, FRIENDS...& **MURDER**

the car. That would be the last time I would see RB.

***

It was Monday morning. Mike and I were in the backyard sitting in the dump truck before we got our work assignment for the day. I was reading *The Legacy Tribune* newspaper like I always do each morning. I would read the sports section and then I would read the local news section.

On this day, I read an article that caught my attention:

The Legacy Tribune

BODY OF MAN FOUND

¶SANTA MONICA, CA - Homicide investigators are looking into the death of an unidentified black man whose body was found...at approximately 12:15 pm by hospital security officers. "We are treating it at this point as a homicide...the victim had trauma to the body. The cause of death is to be determined by an autopsy."

The body was that of a 6-foot-tall, approximately 220-pound man in his late 20s to early 30s.

After reading the article, I mentioned to Mike what I had just read. I told him that I thought it was sad.

"It's a trip," I told him.

"Why do you think it's a trip?" he asked.

"Whoever they found is a Black guy and he is around the same age as me."

At the time, I was 30 years old.

"That could have been me or one of the homies," I said.

"You're right. He's somebody's son, friend,

maybe brother, or father, but you never know. People out here in these streets hold no regard for human life," Mike said.

"You're right," I told Mike and threw the newspaper on the dashboard of the truck.

***

Later that day when I got home from work, I was in the backyard feeding the dogs when I received a 911 text from Top.

I stopped feeding the dogs right away and went into the house to call him.

"Hey, Top. What's up?"

"When's the last time you talked to or seen Devin?"

"I talked to him within the past few days," I told him.

"When?" I started to think and then he said, "Detectives just left Devin's house and they were asking the neighbors if they recognized some deceased person in a photo."

Top lived down the street from Devin and had known him for many years. Top was about five years younger than me. We met in 1992 when we drove school buses together. He was the homie and part of my crew – HOMIES, *Lovers*, FRIENDS.

I started HOMIES, *Lovers*, FRIENDS (HLF) Party Productions in 1993. It was named after one of R Kelly's songs. I was a huge fan of R Kelly so that name was perfect.

In 1989, three years after high school, my mother moved to Texas and left me her condo. I would have these party functions at my condo almost every weekend. We were young, just having fun like most young adults.

I started inviting my friends over on the weekends. We would listen to music, play cards, dominoes, and play drinking games. Eventually things evolved into full blown parties beyond the condo. It was a major production and a brotherhood amongst those who were involved. Top was one of the younger homies.

"Some neighbors were saying the picture looked like Devin. But because no one is home at his mother's house, he couldn't be identified."

I was stunned. I started thinking about the last time I spoke to or saw Devin.

"I talked to Devin on Saturday, for sure," I told Top. "I'll call you back."

When I got off the phone, I tried calling Devin, but his phone went straight to voicemail. At that point, I started to worry. I called him a few more times and got nothing. I didn't know what else to do, so I started calling the other homies.

The first person that came to my mind was RB. I realized that RB might have been the last person to see Devin.

When he answered, I asked, "Hey RB, when is the last time you talked to Devin?"

"I haven't talked to Devin since Saturday.

The last time I saw him he was talking to a dude in an orange jumpsuit."

This was the same thing RB had told me on Saturday.

I didn't tell him what Top had just told me because I didn't want any rumors to get started, so I just said ok and hung up. I called Shawn, Dontae, Tank, and anybody else who might have talked to Devin on the regular. I didn't tell them anything about what I had heard.

In between calling everybody else, I was also calling Devin and leaving messages. I paged him, sent 911 text messages so he would call me back, but still nothing.

RIME SCENE - DO NOT CROSS

CHAPTER 9

It was about 6:30 p.m. on Monday. I sat there wondering what the hell was going on with Devin. Then, I remembered the newspaper article I had read earlier that day.

Could that be Devin? I thought.

The body that was found was a Black dude and he was about Devin's age. No one had heard from Devin, and he wasn't returning my calls, so it really could have been him. I hoped not, yet thoughts invaded my mind, and the longer time went on, the more I thought about Devin and the gruesome possibility.

At about 7 p.m., my sister, Dana, came home from work. I was sitting in the living room, just staring at the walls, worried.

"How are you doing, little brother? How was your day?" Dana asked.

I said, "Not good right now, sis."

"What's wrong?" she asked.

"I've been trying to get in touch with Devin for the past few hours because of a phone call that I received from Top. I've been calling and leaving messages, and he hasn't returned any of them."

"What did Top say?"

"Top, who lives down the street from Devin, told me that one of his neighbors said that detectives were knocking on doors, asking people if they recognized a deceased person in a photo. He said the neighbors were saying the person in the photo looked like Devin, but no one could identify him," I explained. "The police also had his truck towed away to check for fingerprints."

I told her about the article I had read and how the person they described seemed like a match to Devin.

She said, "Anthony, you really don't think that could be Devin, do you?"

"Well, why hasn't he called back? Why hasn't anyone heard from him?"

"When was the last time you talked to him?" She probed.

"On Saturday morning. He called and told me he was going to pick up his money from RB. Then, he called Shawn from RB's house because he was supposed to go to the game with us. I haven't heard from him since."

Now, Dana looked worried.

She said, "Anthony, it sounds like something is going on because that doesn't sound like Devin. Should we call the coroner's office to see if that body that was found has been identified yet?"

I thought that was a good idea.

She asked, "Would you like me to call them for you?"

"Yes, sis. Please."

Dana called information to get the number for the Santa Monica Coroner's Office. Someone answered right away.

"Hello, how can I help you?"

"I'm calling for my brother who's concerned about a friend he hasn't spoken to in a few days. He's been calling, leaving messages, and he hasn't returned any of his phone calls. None of his friends have heard from him either, so he's just worried. He also read in the newspaper earlier today that a body was found of a Black man in his late 20s, early 30s," Dana explained.

"He also received a call from a friend saying his other friend's truck had been towed to check for fingerprints. The police apparently had a picture of a body that looked like his friend, but no one could confirm it. So, he wants to know if it could be his friend."

The person on the phone said, "I am sorry to hear about your brother's friend and pray that he's ok. We only pick up bodies and don't examine or identify them. You will have to contact the County Examiner's Office."

They provided her with the number and wished us luck.

Dana hung up the phone and called the County Examiner's Office. When they answered, she told them the same thing. They said she would have to have a full name to help identify the body.

"His full name is Devin Lamont Cole," I told her.

Dana relayed the information and was put on hold. It seemed like it took forever, and we didn't know if that was good or bad.

Finally, after being on hold for about 10 minutes, they came back on the phone. They said they took a lot of fingerprints from his truck and the set of fingerprints that belonged to him matched the body they found on Sunday.

"We are sorry. Please tell your brother that unfortunately the body found is that of Devin Cole. Also, let him know that Devin's parents haven't been notified yet because they haven't been home. You two are the first to know that Devin has passed."

My sister looked at me, nodded her head, and in a low, soft tone said, "Yes, Anthony. It's Devin."

I went into shock. My sister hugged me, and we both cried.

***

That had to be one of the saddest moments of my life, other than my mother passing away in 2013 and losing my two older brothers. Losing Devin is still one of the most heartbreaking moments of all time.

After Dana and I cried, I got myself together. I knew that I had to break the tragic news to my friends. I knew it was going to be a long night.

My first call was to RB, since I knew RB was one of the last people to see Devin alive.

I called him and when he answered, I said, "RB, guess what? You're not going to believe this."

"What?"

"I just found out that Devin is dead."

His exact words were, "What? How did that nigga die?"

I was blown away by his response. I couldn't believe he responded that way, especially after hearing a close friend had passed away. The way he responded *still* bothers me to this day.

"I don't know *how* he died. You tell me!" I told him. "You were one of the last people to see him. None of the homies have talked to him or have seen him since Saturday, since he left your house!"

RB started telling me again that he saw Devin talking to a guy in an orange jumpsuit. He told me that Devin was getting tickets to the game.

"Devin told me he couldn't get any tickets to that game," I reminded him.

He responded by, once again, telling me the story of seeing Devin's truck in the driveway and moving the truck for his dad. He said he got in the truck and noticed Devin's pager was on the seat with missed pages.

"I didn't touch it. I just parked the truck across the street," he said. "Blood! I just remembered something!"

"What?" I asked.

"I touched the truck when I moved it!" he

panicked.

"So, what does that mean?" I asked him.

"My fingerprints are going to be on that truck because I moved it. They're going to think I did it."

"Why in the fuck are you thinking about that? Did *you* do it?!"

"Do what?" RB asked.

"Kill Devin!"

"Fuck, no! I didn't kill Devin!"

"Ok then," I said. "Devin used to let everyone drive his truck, so there's going to be a lot of fingerprints."

He responded in a more relaxed tone, "Yeah, that's right."

Then, I told him I would call him back, but I was still upset by his response. I thought he would be more affected and sincere about the news.

***

I called Shawn and his response was very different. I told Shawn what I knew.

He said, "Ant, you're lying, *right*?"

"No. I just found out from the County Examiner's Office."

He broke down on the phone and said, "Ant, I'll call you back."

I'm sure Shawn didn't want me to hear him crying, so he hung up.

I went on to call Tank, Dontae, Tina,

Hakeem, and Johnny. But it was Hakeem's response that has stuck with me to this day.

I had Tank on the line when I called him.

His exact response was, "What? Devin's *dead*?" in a sarcastic tone.

"RB DID IT! RB DID IT, man! Y'all know RB did it! I told you, Ant! That nigga tried to have me set up! HE'S CRAZY!" Hakeem yelled.

Hakeem was yelling and crying at the same time, just repeating over and over that RB killed Devin. We tried calming him down, but he wasn't having it.

"Where's RB?" he asked.

"The last time I talked to him, he was at home," I told him.

Hakeem was really hurt like the rest of us because Devin was the kind of friend that would give you the shirt off his back. No one would ever expect something like this to happen to him of all people. Hakeem was convinced that RB murdered Devin or set him up.

CRIME SCENE - DO NOT CROSS

CHAPTER 10

It seemed like that night was never going to end. I received a lot of calls about Devin's death. It seemed like I talked to everybody who knew Devin that night and he knew a lot of people.

At one point, me, RB, and Shawn were on the phone, and I remember RB telling Shawn that they should go over to Devin's house.

I asked, "Why?"

RB said, "Because we should go and pay our condolences and respects to the family."

"I don't think that's a good idea," I told them.

"Why?" RB asked.

"I was the first one to find out and Devin's mother doesn't even know her son is dead yet."

RB still kept telling Shawn that they should go. I told them they shouldn't. RB got off the phone and I continued talking to Shawn. He hung up after a while. Against their better judgment, they hooked up and ended up going to Devin's mother's house.

Later, I received a call back from Johnny and what he told me blew me away.

He said, "RB came to my house early Sunday, and he was driving Devin's truck. He wanted me to follow him to Devin's house to drop off his truck and take him home. He told me he had borrowed Devin's truck earlier. Something is not right, Ant. I don't want to be involved in any shit."

"Yea, something sounds fishy," I told him.

***

By this time, Devin's mother, Mrs. Cole, had made it home. Detectives were there waiting for her. My son's mother's sister, and a few other people had gone over there to pay their respects. After breaking the news to Mrs. Cole, she questioned the detectives and everyone at her house.

"Who would want to kill my son, Devin?" she asked.

Then, the doorbell rang. Everyone paused to see who was coming in next. When the door was opened, it was Shawn and RB.

"Can I help you?" Mrs. Cole asked.

RB said, "We came over to pay our respects."

Mrs. Cole told them to come in and asked them, "What did you hear?"

"Devin… he's dead, *right*?" RB responded.

Mrs. Cole replied, "Yes, I just found out my son is gone. How did you guys find out?"

"Anthony told us," RB said.

Mrs. Cole asked, "How does Anthony know?"

RB told her that he didn't know.

Not long after, the detectives separated RB and Shawn. They left Shawn in the living room and took RB outside. They started asking him questions because some of the things he was saying about Devin wasn't adding up.

Mrs. Cole said, "Well, since he's here now,

Shawn…" she said pointing toward the front door where RB was outside, " He came to my house yesterday morning and handed over Devin's keys to his truck."

Shawn spoke up and said, "No, ma'am, my name is Shawn, and his name is RB."

Mrs. Cole said, "No, sweetie. Not you. I'm talking about the other Shawn that's outside talking to the detectives."

Shawn interrupted her again and said, "No, Mrs. Cole. My name is Shawn Deandre Thomas. His name is Roosevelt Aaron Bishop."

Then, Devin's uncle stood up and said, "Hold the fuck up because there's some shit in the game."

By that, he meant something didn't sound right and he wanted answers. The detectives were paying attention, too, and they directed Shawn outside.

While all of this was going on, I called Shawn. I had no idea what they were going through. He told me they were outside Devin's house, being questioned by the police and that some things RB was saying didn't add up.

"The homies are putting on our own investigation and we came up with the conclusion that RB probably knows who killed Devin," I told Shawn. "We think it could've been a deal that went bad, and RB is covering it up."

"I'm thinking the same thing," Shawn responded.

"Where is RB? What is he doing?"

"RB is being questioned, but I think we both have to follow the police to the station for more questioning."

I was pissed off at this point and told Shawn, "You shouldn't have gone with RB."

He said, "I know. I'll call you back after I finish talking with the police."

RIME SCENE - DO NOT CROSS

CHAPTER 11

As Shawn and RB were on their way to the station for questioning, I started getting calls and rumors started to circulate among our friends. I was furious. If only they had listened to me when I told them not to go to Devin's house, these rumors wouldn't have started.

About an hour later, Shawn called me. He had just finished being questioned by the police. He told me he was in and out in no time, but RB was still there and still being questioned.

"RB was talking crazy about Devin, and I don't know why," he told me. "RB was very talkative, saying shit about Devin that I have never heard."

"Be careful and call me when you make it home," I told him.

He said OK and hung up.

About an hour after my phone call with Shawn, I got a call from RB when he got home from the police station. He didn't mention anything about being questioned by detectives; he was talking totally different. It didn't sound like Devin's death was bothering him too much, and I thought that was weird.

Later on, that same night, Detective Morales with the Santa Monica Homicide Unit called me and asked me a few questions. She asked me how I found out about Devin's death, and I explained the whole story to her.

"Could you come down to the station for questioning?" she asked.

I agreed and she told me to come alone and not tell anyone.

It was about 11 p.m. when I got up, got dressed, and headed to the police station. She had told me where to park and which door to come to. When I arrived, it was about 11:45 p.m. I noticed the station was closed and that surprised me because I thought police stations were always open.

I parked where I was told to, got out of my car, and walked to a set of double doors. I called Detective Morales, and she met me at the door to let me in.

"Hello, Mr. Cunningham. How are you holding up?"

"I guess I'm still in shock with everything that's going on," I replied.

"I can only imagine," she said. "Follow me."

It felt weird and creepy because there were only a few detectives in the whole station. She asked me if I wanted anything to drink and I told her no.

"Depending on how the questioning goes, you should be out of here in about an hour," she explained.

We came up to a door that had a 12 by 12 window in it. She opened it and we went inside. I started thinking that this must be an interrogation room. I had never been in one before, but I had seen them on TV. While we were inside, another detective joined us, but I can't remember his name. They told me that they were going to be asking me a few questions about Devin and what I knew about his death. I told them that was ok, then proceeded to tell them everything that I knew from the article I read, to my sister calling the County Examiner's Office. Once they knew that, they started asking me more specific questions about my friendship with Devin.

"How long did you know Devin and how did you meet?"

"I've known Devin for about 10 years, and I met him from hanging out and partying."

"How close were you?"

"Devin and I were real close. We became roommates back in 1992 and were roommates on and off at different locations until 1997."

"Did you and Devin ever have any problems with each other?"

"No! We had a few arguments here and there, but it never came to fist fights. Devin and I got along like brothers, and that's what we were."

"Do you know if Devin had any enemies?"

"Not that I know of," I told them. "Devin was everyone's friend. He would've given you the shirt off his back. He was the kind of guy you would want as a friend. No matter what you needed, Devin would have been there to support you the best way he could. That's why someone murdering him is so crazy because I could never see anyone wanting to hurt Devin."

They started asking about RB and Devin's friendship.

"How long did they know each other?"

I told them, "They probably met around the same time we met."

"How close were RB and Devin?"

I told them, "They were as close as I was with Devin."

"Did RB and Devin ever get into an argument or fight?"

I told them I didn't know. Then they asked, "Do you ever think RB would harm Devin?"

"No."

"Why not?"

"I have known RB for years and I could never see him doing anything like that. Let alone to Devin."

Both of the detectives left the room. They would come back in to check on me from time to time, and eventually they told me I could go home. They told me not to discuss the interrogation with anyone because they were building a case, and no one had been arrested yet. They also told me that I could be called back in for questioning at any time. When I got out of there, it was 1 a.m., I was tired. I got home and went to sleep.

RIME SCENE - DO NOT CROSS

CHAPTER 12

The next day was pretty much the same – more people calling me, talking about what they heard, and what they thought might have happened. I wasn't really trying to talk to too many people because I knew the rumors would continue. I was still hurt and lost, just trying to figure out who could have done this to Devin.

RB would call me throughout the day, asking what I had heard. But mostly he talked about other stuff that had nothing to do with Devin. He would talk about how we all used to hang out, and how he missed those days. He talked about the times when him, Tank, Shawn, and Devin used to go partying on the military base and how they used to meet a lot of girls. That's how he met his girlfriend Peaches.

He told me that they all used to fly to Las Vegas, and everybody would have their own limo and have a lot of fun. I just sat there and listened to him talk. I grew more concerned and worried, too.

Later that evening, when I was talking to RB, he told me that he had to get off the phone and that he would call me back. About an hour later, I received another call from Detective Morales. She wanted me to come back in for more questions. She told me that RB was also there being questioned, and they didn't want him to know that I was coming in.

They told me where to park again and this time they asked me if RB knew what kind of car

I drove. I told them yes and they told me to park in the front, since he would leave out of the back.

Shit was getting crazy. It felt like something out of a movie. When I got inside the police station, it was closed once again. The only people there were the detectives interrogating us. They had RB in one room, and they didn't want him to see me. They left me in a room until they could move him through the hallway so he wouldn't know I was there.

I tell you, that shit was crazy! That night I remember very well.

It was that night they asked me, "Did you tell RB that Devin was shot twice in the back of the head?"

"I am not sure if I told him that."

"Who told you that?"

"I am not sure who told me that because I have talked to so many people over the past two days."

"If you told RB that and you don't know who told you that, then you will be looked at as one of the suspects."

"Are you serious? You can't be serious, right?"

The detective said, "Yes, we are very serious. We haven't gone public with how Devin was killed."

"I didn't have shit to do with Devin being killed!" I firmly stated.

The detective told me, "You better find out

who told you or you might be getting arrested and charged."

They also told me that RB's story wasn't adding up or matching with anyone else's. They advised me not to talk to him anymore.

"You don't have to worry about that because I see exactly what he is doing," I said.

"If you remember who told you about Devin, call us, no matter how late."

I left the police station late again, around midnight this time. RB was already gone by the time I left, so they weren't worried about him seeing me.

When I got home that night, I started calling everyone who I might have talked to about Devin. I asked all of them if they were the ones who told me about how Devin was killed. They all told me no.

Finally, I called my son's mother, Tina, and told her what the detectives told me. The response I received blindsided me.

She said, "I told you that."

"What?"

"Yeah, I told you because Jessica was at Devin's mother's house when the detectives told his mom."

"That's right! She was there. She was also with Devin the night before he died, so it makes sense."

I felt so relieved, and I couldn't wait to get off the phone with Tina to call Detective Morales.

It had to be about 1:30 a.m. when I called and told her. Since she was the lead detective on the case, she had a list of people who were at Devin's mother's house when they broke the news to Mrs. Cole.

I told her that I knew who told me and she asked, "Who?"

"It was my son's mother, Tina, and her sister, Jessica."

She looked at her list and saw Jessica's name and told me that I was clear.

That night, I received a call from RB. He lied about going on a date. He didn't know that I had been at the police station, too. I told him I had to get off of the phone and that was the last time I talked to him. I guess he was feeling like I knew something was going on because he never called again, either.

***

The rest of the week was crazy with more rumors and speculations on what happened to Devin and who was involved. No arrest was made during that time, so no one really knew anything. As far as we knew, Devin's killer was still on the streets.

Funeral arrangements were made for Devin the following week and all the homies attended, except RB. That made him look even more suspicious. Rumors had circulated that he had left and moved out of the state where his mother lived, but no one had talked to him to confirm that.

I stayed in touch with Detective Morales. She told me that they were working on the case and if anything came up that she would contact me. I didn't hear back from her for a couple of months.

RIME SCENE - DO NOT CROSS

CHAPTER 13

A few months went by. We still hadn't heard from anyone about Devin's case, and no arrests had been made. It had been confirmed that RB was living out of state. He also had a court day in January, for something else, but he was a no-show.

Since Lola was the one who bailed him out, she was responsible for him being in court. Since he did not show up, the court issued a warrant for his arrest. They also put pressure on Lola to find him and bring him to court to face his charges. Lola couldn't find RB, so she hired a private investigator to help bring him back to Santa Monica to attend court.

The whole month of January went by and there was no sign of RB. February came and something happened that only God could explain. Devin's mother, Mrs. Cole, received one of Devin's bank statements. I know there's nothing unusual about that, but there was something unusual about that specific statement. It showed usage and charges in Mobile, Alabama.

Mrs. Cole was confused because she knew that her son had been deceased for a while. Now, she was receiving her son's bank statements showing her son's credit card being used in Mobile. She contacted the detectives right away and they came by to look at the bank statement.

They gathered some information on where

the credit card was being used and they got in touch with the private investigator. They gave him the information they had gathered from Mrs. Cole, and he went to Mobile, Alabama to check things out.

This time, the private investigator was successful. He found the casino where the card was being used. He found surveillance cameras and some signed documents that led him and police officers to RB's mother's house. The police, along with the private investigator, knocked on the door and an older Black woman answered the door.

"Can I help you?" she inquired.

"We are looking for Mr. Roosevelt Aaron Bishop."

"Why? Who wants to know?" she pushed back.

"We want to know. We need to talk to him. He has a warrant out for his arrest in Santa Monica, California," they told her. "It's also possible that he could be involved in a homicide case."

"Well, my son hasn't been involved in any homicide. And he's not here," she stated.

"Is it ok if we come inside and search his room?" they asked.

"Not without a search warrant you can't," she replied.

"We will be back with the search warrant."

She said ok, and two hours later, the police

and private investigator returned with the warrant.

They knocked on the door, showed Mrs. Bishop the warrant, and told her they had to search RB's room.

She let them in, and they asked her which room was RB's. She pointed to one of the rooms at the back of the house. As they searched RB's room, Mrs. Bishop just stood there in disbelief. Mrs. Bishop was a nice, hardworking woman from what I can remember, and RB was her only son. He also had an older sister.

RB's mom and dad divorced before I met him, but from what I heard and remember, his dad was still in his life. RB was his dad's only son and he pretty much got what he wanted as far as I can remember. RB's mom owned a house in Malibu, California and she lived alone until she moved to Mobile, Alabama in the mid-90s.

The police and the private investigator ended their search in Mrs. Bishop's home. Shockingly, they found a few items that belonged to Devin, including his credit card, which led them there, his camcorder, video tapes, and a few other items, along with a one-way Greyhound bus ticket stub.

They approached Mrs. Bishop and asked her, "Where is RB?"

"He works for UPS, but he didn't do anything wrong."

"He will have his time in court. If he didn't

do anything wrong, then he will be a free man. But for now, he is getting arrested."

***

The police and private investigator found the UPS location where RB was working and placed him under arrest. The news broke in Santa Monica, California that RB was arrested in Mobile, Alabama and was being extradited.

It had been months and Devin's case had gone cold. When the news broke that they had arrested RB, I think it was more of a relief. Everyone had pretty much concluded that he had something to do with Devin's murder.

CRIME SCENE - DO NOT CROSS

CHAPTER 14

About a week later, it all hit me. I broke down. I couldn't believe everything that had happened. It was like a nightmare or something you see in the movies or on TV.

I started reminiscing about all the fun we used to have. From the house parties, hanging out, the college campus parties, going to L.A., hanging out in San Diego, softball games, football games, cookouts, fixing up our cars, and cruising up and down the road. I mean, you name it, we did it.

We were a fun group of people to be around, and everyone wanted to hang out with us. We were a special group of hardworking people just enjoying life, raising our kids. We had women and men in our group, **HOMIES,** *Lovers,* & FRIENDS. I thought our friendship would last forever.

I never imagined anything like this would happen. I don't think anyone thought it would have happened to us, especially to Devin. Now, with RB behind bars, everyone could rest and not worry about him being out there free.

***

RB was charged with second-degree murder. It was crazy seeing his face plastered all over the news every day in the Legacy Tribune. I mean, this was someone that we all personally knew, but if he really committed the crime, he deserved every bit of the time and more.

The District Attorney (D.A.) reached out to me and informed me of who would be the lead prosecutor in the State vs. Roosevelt Bishop case. The D.A. wanted to set up an appointment with me. She said I could go to her office, or she could come to my house.

"You can come to my house. I can give you pictures and videos of events we all did together," I told her.

She agreed, came to my house, and she interviewed me about the case she was building against RB.

"I organized our group. It's made up of women and men. Most of us have known each other for 10 years or more, so we are a tight knit group," I explained. "I came up with the group **HOMIES,** *Lovers*, & FRIENDS back in 1992. I use it whenever we have any kind of function."

"How long did you know Devin and RB?" she inquired.

"I knew both of them for about 12 years."

She pretty much asked me the same questions the detectives asked me, so I knew what to expect. She was asking more questions about our friendship and wanted to know how close we were.

"We were more like brothers than friends. I think of it as more of a brotherhood, one that could never be broken."

I shared some photos and videos that I had taken over the years. There were a lot because I kept my camcorder and camera with me at all times.

"Since you put the group together and everyone has stayed in touch with you, you will be the most important witness in this case," the D.A. told me.

"I am fine with that. I want justice for Devin, his family, and his friends. He didn't deserve to die, especially when all he was trying to do was help a friend."

I met with the D.A. a few more times before the trial started. I remember when she wanted Hakeem, Shawn, and myself to come to her office in downtown Santa Monica.

The trial started during the summer of 1998, and there were several people who took the witness stand. The key witnesses were Devin's girlfriend, Tank, Shawn, Peaches as she was called, RB's aunt Sheila, and me.

RB's ex-girlfriend, Peaches, testified that one of the blankets wrapped around Devin's body looked like the one she and RB bought on a trip to Mexico. She also testified that one time she had a doctor's appointment and RB was there with her son. The doctor called her back, and RB stayed in the lobby with her son. When she came back to the lobby, RB and her son were gone. She said she was wondering where they went and walked by the window to look outside. She spotted RB and her son walking in the parking lot. She said she didn't know why they were out there, but later she found out that was the same parking lot where Devin's body was found.

When I was called to testify against RB, all eyes were on me because everyone knew how close I was to RB and Devin. Everyone wanted to hear my testimony.

The D.A. asked me questions for information that only I knew. He asked about conversations I had with Hakeem and Devin and many more things. RB sat on the left side of the courtroom, next to his attorney. The day I testified, RB wore a yellow, short-sleeved shirt. I noticed whenever I was being questioned, RB would start doodling. When I would talk, he would stop and listen to what I had to say, because it was the first time he had heard what I actually knew. He would then lean over toward his attorney and shake his head, whispering his disagreement in his ear.

RIME SCENE - DO NOT CROSS

CHAPTER 15

While on recess, I was in the hallway when Peaches approached me.

"So, you're Ant?" she asked.

"Yes."

"My name is Skyla. You probably know me as Peaches."

"Yes, I just saw your testimony. You're RB's girlfriend, right?"

"Well, his ex-girlfriend."

"Yes, that's right."

She then said, "I have heard so much about you. Now I can put a face to the name."

"I hope whatever you heard was good," I said, making her laugh.

She responded, "RB never had anything bad to say about you."

"Well, I guess that's nice to know."

Skyla went on to tell me how she first met RB when he was with Tank, Shawn, and Devin. She told me when they first met, RB was nice to her, but over the years, he changed and started abusing her for no reason. She told me that RB was a violent guy and that she feared him.

Once again, I couldn't believe what I was hearing. I never saw that side of him. She said that he would even hit her in front of her son and that one time, RB got upset with her son and picked him up like he was going to hurt him. She said he got so upset and kicked them both out of the apartment and locked them out, but he finally let them back in.

"You don't know RB like you think you do," she told me.

"I guess I don't," I responded.

She told me what led her to call the police on him that Halloween night when he was arrested. She told me that RB was abusing her the whole nine months she was pregnant. She said when he got upset with her, he would make a certain sound. When he did that, she knew she was about to get hit.

She said she couldn't take it anymore, so she finally kicked him out. The day of his arrest, he told her he needed to borrow some money and asked if she could drop it off. She said the only reason she did was because she felt sorry for him, and he was the father of her daughter.

But she had warned him before that if he ever put his hands on her again, she was going to call the police.

"I went by his apartment, but I told him I wasn't coming in. I told him he could come down to the car and get the money," she said. "He came down, sat in the car, and we started talking. Everything was fine. But after I gave him the money, he started yelling at me and being disrespectful. I told him it was time for me to go, and that's when he hit me."

She told me that she fought him off enough to get away, and when she ran across the street and into the Leasing Office, the people inside called 911. She said five minutes later, RB came inside the office and sat down as if nothing happened. He stayed there until the police came and arrested him.

I couldn't believe it. I sat there trippin because this was the first time I heard how everything started. Devin Cole is gone all because of the story she had just told me (RB was arrested for attacking Skyla, he needed bail money, Hakeem lent the bail money, RB was not able to pay it back, Devin tried to help RB and simply wanted his money back and was murdered.) The crazy part about it, I had never met Skyla before this.

I felt bad for her just like I felt bad for Devin's family and Devin's one-year-old and four-year-old sons. It's crazy how one person can destroy so many lives for generations and years to come and that's exactly what RB did based on the evidence.

***

During the whole trial, RB made no effort to answer questions. He even turned away from the inquiring faces of all his friends. RB showed no remorse and I think that's what made everyone upset.

"Devin was always a friend to you," Devin's girlfriend said, facing RB in court. "What could he have said to you that was so wrong? RB, I really hope you find it in your heart someday to let someone know because you took someone away who loved you like a brother."

RB just stood there, facing the judge not turning around once.

Shawn got up and said, "RB, you and I have known each other since we were eight years old. We both only have sisters, no brothers, so *we* were like brothers. We used to stay the night at each other's houses, we played football together, we went to high school together. We even remained friends all the way up until you took Devin from us. You even placed the blame on me and said I had something to do with it. You had Devin's family look at me crazy! All I have to say, if I had anything to do with what you did to Devin, turn around and face his family and tell them what part I played."

RB stood there facing the judge. He never turned around.

Shawn continued, "Man, you hurt so many people, but where you're going, you will have a long enough time to think about it. I suggest you find religion while you're in prison. Ask God for forgiveness because you took a man who was well-loved by so many."

You can tell by the tears flowing down Shawn's face that he was heartbroken by what RB did.

RB also had someone speak up on his behalf during the trial – his aunt Sheila. She questioned what happened and whether or not RB shot Devin or if others were involved. But all the evidence pointed straight to him.

RB was the last person to see Devin alive, he was the one who drove his truck back to his mother's house, and he dropped off his keys. He took Devin's items from his room, then used his credit card in another state. All the evidence pointed to him!

RIME SCENE - DO NOT CROSS

CHAPTER 16

The case was ending, and it wasn't looking good for RB. The judge handed the case over to the jury. Two days after the trial started, the jury came back with a second-degree murder charge and the judge sentenced RB to 25 years to life.

Devin was shot twice in the back of the head and once in the shoulder in RB's apartment over a $1,500 loan. Although RB never testified, he told a probation officer that he shot Devin in self-defense when they got into a fight at his apartment. He said that Devin was pressuring him to participate in a check scam.

The murder weapon was never recovered, however RB told authorities that he threw the gun in the ocean after he shot Devin. RB served his sentence in Centinela State Prison in Imperial, California. He was paroled and released in September of 2019 after only serving 21 years.

We learned a lot during and after that trial. Based on court documents, Devin made it to RB's house and an argument ensued at some point. RB then retrieved his gun and shot Devin in his upper right shoulder as he was trying to leave. The shot to his shoulder wasn't fatal, but it hit his vertebrae and put him down.

That's when RB stood over him and shot his best friend twice in the back of the head, close-range, execution style. RB then took Devin's truck keys and drove to his mother's house. He knocked on her door and told Mrs.

Cole that they switched cars. He said that Devin wanted him to pick up his gaming system, camcorder, and video tapes.

Devin's mother let him in to get those things, and RB took more than he said he came for. His hands were full when he left, and Mrs. Cole asked if he wanted a bag. Before he left, Mrs. Cole told RB to remind Devin of his uncle's reception that was happening later that evening. RB said he would tell him.

According to receipts that were recovered, RB pawned Devin's things. After he left the pawn shop, he headed back to his apartment where Devin's lifeless body remained. That's when he called Shawn and I to see if he could go to the game with us.

When Shawn and RB arrived back to Shawn's house, he was wearing a white T-shirt, Guess jeans and some white Nike shoes. When I first saw RB, I asked him where Devin was. That's when he made up the lie about Devin talking to some guy that had an orange jumpsuit on. He was trying to throw us off.

RB had no idea that I knew Devin was coming to his house to pick up his money, so he looked surprised. He then told me that Devin said he was going to pick up some tickets to the game and I told him that Devin said he couldn't get any tickets. RB wouldn't say much more after that.

When he took out that wad of money to pay

for the game ticket, that was supposed to be Devin's ticket, I figured he paid Devin. I had no idea he had shot and killed him.

When I had asked Shawn and RB that night if they wanted to go to the club, RB said he needed to take care of something. It was that night or the next morning when RB used Devin's truck to dump his body in the alley of a hospital. RB then drove to Johnny's house and woke him up.

He mentioned to Johnny that Devin let him borrow his truck and he wanted to know if he could follow him to Devin's to drop it off. Johnny agreed, not knowing what RB had just done. That's why, when I called and told Johnny about Devin's death and that RB might be involved, he had already figured that out.

When they got to Devin's house, RB parked Devin's truck, got out, and walked up to Devin's door. He knocked on the door and Devin's younger brother opened the door. RB gave him Devin's keys. RB turned around and walked toward the street where Johnny was waiting in his truck, but before he reached the truck, someone other than Devin's little brother saw him.

He asked who it was, and he said his name was Shawn because that is what RB told Devin's little brother. That's why, when Shawn and RB went over to pay their respects, she remembered when he dropped the truck off. RB tried to place the blame on Shawn, his lifelong best friend. He tried to get everyone else involved, yet based on the evidence, he committed the murder alone.

After RB dropped off Devin's truck, Johnny dropped him off at home and that's when he started calling me and telling me how he was out walking that morning near Devin's house. He mentioned seeing Johnny, and even mentioned how his truck was parked and Devin's pager was sitting on the seat.

He was looking for an alibi, but it didn't work. Knowing that RB had gone over to Devin's house three times after killing Devin is insane and cold-hearted, especially after facing Mrs. Coles two of those three times. It is unbelievable and heartless, but they say most killers, after they commit a murder, like to return to the murder scene. They like to be around people to get the latest on what's being heard and that's exactly what RB was doing.

He was calling me every single day just to find out what I heard and what was being said. When his name started circulating around the city among family and close friends, he fled. The detectives said that, when RB left for Alabama, they had a hard time accessing his apartment. The front door had been barricaded, so they think he left through the window.

When they finally got in, they found evidence that linked him to the murder, but it wasn't enough at the time. They claimed they never found the smoking gun. The strongest evidence they found in the apartment was a large amount of blood underneath the carpet pad, but on top of the concrete pad.

One night they came in and placed luminol near the front door, on the walls, and on the back of the couch. That is when they found blood splotches on the back of the couch and the wall. They couldn't figure out why there wasn't anything on the floor, though. They turned on the lights and one detective noticed how the shag carpet was cut into a square piece. He pulled it up and you could see where RB had wiped the top of the carpet pad clean. But what he didn't do was pull up the carpet pad and clean the concrete underneath. All this time, they were stepping on the spot where Devin got shot and didn't know it.

Throughout the years, the only friend who had any contact with RB was Dontae. He has talked to him on a few occasions, while he was locked up, and a few times since he's been out.

In the summer of 2022, Dontae said he was at a park near Venice Beach at a dog show when RB, out of nowhere, came up to him and tapped him on the shoulder. He started talking to him as if nothing had ever happened. He said RB was wearing all blue, head to toe, and if he didn't know any better, he would have thought RB was a crip. RB grew up in a neighborhood of Blood gang members. Even though RB was never a gang member, he was affiliated with the Bloods because of where he grew up. The color he represented was red, so it was unusual of him to be wearing all blue.

Dontae said RB was with a Hispanic woman who RB claimed to be his wife. He said RB kept telling his wife how much he missed hanging out with the homies and how we all used to kick it. Dontae said he was in shock and didn't know what to say. He wanted to talk to him about Devin, but he knew it wasn't the right time.

Dontae told me that RB said he lived somewhere near LA. RB mentioned that he drives trucks and comes to Santa Monica from time to time. Dontae said that he left because he felt uncomfortable being around RB. He called Shawn and me to tell us that he saw RB and I think we all were shocked that he was back in Santa Monica, in plain sight like nothing happened.

***

It is now 2023. It's been 26 years since Devin was murdered. I can honestly say that what RB did has had an impact on everyone's life that was close to him. It especially impacted Devin's kids, who never had a chance to see how great their father was.

Things have never been the same with

HOMIES, *Lovers,* & FRIENDS since Devin's murder. Something that started out with love, trust, and brotherhood is no longer there. I used to enjoy having functions and inviting my friends over. But I no longer have those desires.

Nowadays, who can you trust? I find myself staring at the walls of my home, reminiscing, torn between the highs of H L F and the lows, which includes losing two friends. Because at the of the day that is what happened. I lost Devin to death, and I lost RB to prison. From that, trust was shattered.

There were so many joyful memories, but they are stained by this tragedy. Everyone who knew Devin will forever miss him, his wit, charm, and the true friend that he was. At the same time, we were left with so many questions and no answers as it relates to RB. What could bring someone so close to us all to murder one of his own? Did he really do it? The facts say so.

When I started H L F, it was something that I envisioned having forever. But the murder of my friend, Devin Cole, killed that dream. Who would have guessed this is how it would end –

HOMIES, *Lovers,* FRIENDS…
& **MURDER.**

3

IME SCENE - DO NOT CROSS

ABOUT THE AUTHOR

PATRICK L TURNER

Patrick L. Turner was born in Fort Worth, Texas, and relocated to California when he was a young boy. He became a long-time resident of San Diego, California, where he attended and graduated from Morse High School. Patrick played football in high school and in college, later becoming a football coach and youth mentor. He is the youngest of nine children and was raised by a single mother. Patrick personally knows the struggles of being a single parent because he raised his son, Marquis, and his nephew, Bryan. He assumed full-time care of Bryan when he was just seven years old.

Patrick was very active in both Marquis and Bryan's lives, keeping both of them active in local youth sports. While they played youth football, Patrick coached. As a coach, he saw many kids who didn't have the same kind of guidance and support he provided to Marquis and Bryan. In June of 2012, Patrick started the Pat on the Back Foundation (POTB). This project was born from his desire to serve the kids he worked with and others in the community, including under privileged youth. He wanted to 'give back' to his community. The mission of the foundation is simply that - just giving back.

The POTB Foundation maintained a commitment to support disadvantaged and at-risk youth of all ages. In the first six months of its inception, the foundation assisted more than 4,000 youth in the community. Through the foundation, Patrick sponsored sports participation, and educational, historic, and sports related field trips for the community youth. He received many accolades and awards for his work and service, including the Presidential Volunteer Service Award from the administrative office of President Barack Obama.

A distinguished gentleman, Patrick is a serial entrepreneur who has managed several successful businesses over the last 30+ years, including PT Print Productions, PT Limo Party Bus, PT World Travel &

Tours, and PT's Baja Lobster Run (to name a few). In light of his many business ventures, he has been a government employee for almost 30 years. A business major while in college, Patrick is a natural visionary, and he is an innovative businessman with a big heart. He is a proud father and grandfather. He is a loyal Raiders fan, who enjoys traveling, and he currently makes his home in Texas.

Patrick's debut book, HOMIES, *Lovers*, FRIENDS...& **MURDER**, became #1 Bestselling New Release on Amazon.com in June 2023 during the book's presale. Shortly after, he co-founded the Legacy Book Club (LBC), currently a virtual Facebook group that provides an open platform for avid readers to discuss books, especially books by indie authors, like him.

Now a bestselling author, Patrick is currently working on his second book. He continues to manage multiple businesses with plans to take each project to the next level. When asked where his motivation comes from, Patrick shed that his heart's desire has always been to simply make his mother (RIP) proud. Given his success to date, one can assume that she would in fact be extremely proud of him. For booking, speaking engagements, bulk book orders, and more information or to contact Patrick, visit:

www.patricklturner.com

Intro quote borrowed from the lyrics of *"Everybody"* by Boosie Badazz and MO3
Songwriters: Melvin Noble / Zykerian Hood

Patrick "PT" Turner in 1993 at the Jackie Robinson YMCA.

Growing up and being young in the 90's was no easy task. This was the peak of gang banging and dope slangin. I met P.T. in the beginning of the 90's when we were driving school buses. Fresh out of high school, we worked at the same company. I noticed this dude with a Jheri curl who looked like he was the lead singer of Ready for the World (the R&B band from Michigan) or in the group Full Force (from New York)!

As time went by, we became friends. We had the same interest in music, cars, and culture. We were basically living in the same neighborhood area, and we knew some of the same people, so we hit it off. Working with him was a daily highlight because it made the job fun. Other bus drivers who were comedians kept us in good spirits with the clownin on the radio!!!

I was a youngster who saw what drug dealers and gangsters were sporting like jewelry, clothes, cars, and I wanted that too. I wasn't a drug dealer or a gangster, and neither was P.T., but he had all of that – jewelry, clothes, and cars. I learned that he worked for what he had!!! That made me work harder for what I wanted.

P.T. showed me and others that if you work hard you too can have nice things legally!!! He is definitely a good role model and by that he kept me and my lil homies out of trouble. He would let me, and my friends kick it with him and his crew. We appreciated that. He let us be in H.L.F. and we were proud of that because they were older than us. He could have told us youngsters to kick rocks, but he didn't.

We would be up at the swap meet on the weekends and out at the beaches. Many weekends were spent at his famous house parties that are considered legendary!!! Celebrities and legendary DJs were there.

P.T. has this personality that brings all kinds of people together. So, when people heard about a P.T. Production going down EVERYBODY was going to be there!!! Mind you this was way before the internet. This man just made things happen and it was fun!!

I had some of the best times and made the best memories in my life because of him!!! I took some pages out of his book when it comes to being of service to the community. The things this man has done for the youth unselfishly and did it on his own is nothing but incredible. He is an inspiration to me and many more who want to make a POSITIVE impact in this world. He is the definition of "When you put your mind to it........"

We made a lot of friendships with the older homies from H.L.F. It felt like family - real talk!!! The OG'S looked out for us and didn't let anything happen to us. They taught us how to be men and to navigate in situations. Some of those friendships still exist some 40 + years later!!!

P.T. has shown me that you can do and have anything you want if you work for it. Alot of people see him as a boaster, show off, self-centered, egotistical, it's not like that – he's not like that. He's just showing us that a kid from the hood can make it in this world with determination, will, focus, and hard work.

Thank you, brotha, for being that guy!!!

Respect,

> *~DJ*
> *An original member of H L F*

Made in the USA
Las Vegas, NV
14 August 2023

76076981R00083